GREECE

MACEDONIA
EPIRUS
MT. OLYMPUS
THESSALIA
AETOLIA
DELPHI
ACHAIA
ELIS
ARKADIA
ARGOS
ARGOLIS
MESSENIA
LAKONIA
PELOPONNESUS
THEBES
ATTICA
ATHENS
EUBOEA
ÆGEAN SEA
LESBOS
CHIOS
ANDROS
SERIPHOS
NAXOS
SAMOS
MELOS
MYSIA
IONIA
LYDIA
CARIA
CRETE
CNOSSUS
RHODES
MEDITERRANEAN SEA

FOLK TALES OF THE WORLD

GREECE

A.W.Crown

Illustrations by Dean Mitchell

HOUGHTON MIFFLIN COMPANY · BOSTON

New York   Atlanta   Geneva, Ill.   Dallas   Palo Alto

CONTENTS

COPYRIGHT © 1964 E. J. ARNOLD & SON LIMITED LEEDS ENGLAND

All Rights Reserved

Merit Book Edition 1967

HOUGHTON MIFFLIN COMPANY

The Story of Atalanta

Once upon a time there was a king and queen of Arcadia who were very sad indeed. They possessed much wealth, land and many servants, but the gods had not favored them with a child. King Iasus and his wife prayed daily to the gods to send them a baby boy, but for some years their prayers were not answered, and his sorrow was so great that very often King Iasus would shut himself up in his palace and not speak to anyone at all.

One day, as the king was returning from a hunt, he was met by the queen, who was very excited indeed. "Our prayer has been heard," she said, "for today I saw a vision in which I was told that a child will be born to us. Let us offer a sacrifice to the gods in thankfulness for their kindness."

"Your news makes me very happy," said Iasus, "but I hope the child is a boy, for I have set my heart on having a son to reign over my kingdom when I am gone, a son who will bring honor and glory to the land."

"I would be content with a girl child," replied his queen, "for it would be a blessing to me who has no children at all."

As she said this, however, she saw the angry look which came over the face of King Iasus, and she hoped for his sake that the child would be a boy. You can imagine his rage and disappointment when one day a servant came fearfully into his room to tell him that a baby girl had been born. "I will not have her in my palace," stormed the king, white with anger and bitter disappointment. "The child must be taken away and left to die on the mountains. The gods have laughed at me and made a jest of my prayers. I will not have a girl in my home."

"Let her stay," pleaded the queen, who had already named the baby Atalanta. "Let her stay with me, for I love the child, even though she is such a great disappointment to you."

"She will not stay here," thundered the furious Iasus. "I will not be the jest of my kindgom or of the gods."

He ordered his servants to seize the baby and carry it to the top of a very wild and lonely mountain called Mount Parthenius. "Leave her there," he ordered, "to the mercy of the wolves and the bears. We shall see what will become of this gift of the gods."

The servants dared not disobey their angry master, and Atalanta was wrapped in a cloak and taken to the top of the mountain. There she was placed in a hollow of the rocks, and the servants, hardening their hearts to the weeping of the baby, left her to the mercy of the wild animals which roamed the district.

They had hardly descended the mountain when a fearful growling was heard, and a great she-bear lumbered out of the wooded slopes to see what strange creature the men had left behind. Little Atalanta held up her tiny arms, and the bear, which had just lost her own young ones, licked her soothingly with her warm tongue. Then she carried the baby to her cave, where she kept her warm and fed her. In this way Atalanta grew up strong and fearless, being cared for by the bear which loved her as if she were her own bear cub. The little girl learned how to look after herself, and became very skilled in all the arts of hunting. She could run very quickly too, and often took a delight in chasing the mountain deer, for she ran so swiftly that she could easily outrun them.

One day some hunters, who had been out chasing a deer, came across the little girl, whom they found sleeping on a grassy slope. They were amazed when they saw the child lying there alone and unprotected. As they stood gazing at her in wonderment, she awoke, and startled at the appearance of the men, was about to run away. "Fear not, little child," they said. "We will not harm you. Tell us who you are and we will take you to your home." Little Atalanta could not answer them, nor could she understand what they were saying, for she had never heard the voices of men before, nor did she know their language.

Seeing that she could not understand what they were saying, they made signs to her to show that they were friends, and Atalanta saw that they did not mean to do her any harm. She was very curious too, and when they took her hand, she made no attempt to struggle away from them, but went with them to the rough home in which they lived.

Here she lived with the hunters until she was quite grown up. They took her hunting with them, and taught her how to shoot with the bow and arrow. She became so skilled at shooting that her arrow never missed, and often she would be the only one to return successfully from the hunt. One creature she would never shoot at, however, was the bear, nor would she allow the hunters to do so either, for it was a bear which had saved her from a terrible fate and brought her up on lonely Mount Parthenius.

As the years went by, the story of a strange girl who had been brought up by a bear on Mount Parthenius reached the ears of King Iasus, and he began to wonder if this girl was the child he had ordered to be carried there. "If indeed she is Atalanta," he said, "then she must have been saved by the will of the gods. I am getting old, and there is no male child to take charge of my kingdom. Perhaps if she marries, a male child may be born to her and I shall have my wish after all."

He ordered a search to be made for Atalanta, and declared that when found she was to be brought before him. It was not long before the searchers found her living with the hunters and she was brought before King Iasus. Atalanta was not in the least nervous or afraid of the king, and she stood before him, calm and beautiful, as he told her who she really was, and why he had condemned her to be left on the mountain.

"I wish you now to remain with us at the palace," he said, "for I see that it is the will of the gods that you remain alive. I want you, however, to agree to marry a man whom I will choose for you, so that one day there will be a male child to rule my kingdom."

"I will remain," said Atalanta, who had no real love for the father who had left her to die on the mountain, "but if you wish me to marry, I will make the conditions. The man I marry must be able to run more swiftly than I can, and those who try and do not succeed must be put to death."

Now Atalanta knew that her fame as a runner was well known and secretly she hoped that no man would risk losing his life, for she did not wish to please King Iasus. The king, however, could not believe that his daughter could run more swiftly than any man, and he thought that the girl was just being conceited. "I will agree to your request," he said, "and any man who loses his race against you will be put to death."

Many men did indeed try, for Atalanta was exceedingly beautiful, but she ran with the speed of the wind, and each of

her unhappy suitors was slain when the race was over, and King Iasus was in despair.

One day, a very handsome young man named Melanion heard of the beauty of Atalanta, and decided to try to win her as his bride. He practised running for many days, and before long became the equal of the swiftest runners in the country. His friends, however, tried to stop him from running against the sure-footed princess. "No matter how swiftly you can run," they said, "you will never outrun her, and you are just throwing your life away."

"Nevertheless I will try," he replied, "for she is so beautiful that I will gladly risk my life to marry her."

In due course he appeared at the court of King Iasus, and presented himself as a suitor for the hand of Atalanta. The king spoke to him very sadly. "You are young and strong," he said, "but you must know that many men have tried to win her and failed. They have all been put to death. Why not give up this useless race and return to your people? If you do race and lose, then I must order your death, for no mercy can be shown once the race is run."

"I am not afraid to die," replied the bold Melanion, "but I am certain that I can outrun your daughter. Let the race be arranged."

"It shall be done," said Iasus, "but remember that once the race begins, no mercy can be shown to you."

That night, as Melanion was preparing for sleep, quite unworried by the fact that he might not live another day, there appeared before him the goddess Aphrodite, the goddess of love and beauty. She had been stirred by the bravery of Melanion and his love for Atalanta, and had decided to help him win the race.

"You are brave and bold, O Melanion," she said, "and deserve the favor of the gods. You will win the race tomorrow if you do as I ask. Here are three golden apples which you must take with you. Now it is the custom of Atalanta to give a good start to those racing against her, for she is always sure of overtaking them. This she will do to you too. When you hear her approaching, drop one of the apples on the ground. The apples are enchanted, and she will be so entranced by them that she will stop to pick them up. That will give you a chance to race ahead, and when she approaches a second time drop the second apple and then the third. This will delay her a great deal, but you must not stop. You must race for dear life, for even though she may stop for a moment, she will catch up easily if you hesitate even for a glance behind you. Take the apples," she said, "and the blessing of Aphrodite go with you."

The next day, thousands of people came from far and wide to watch the race. Some shook their heads sadly when they saw the brave Melanion take up his position ready for the starting signal. "The princess has given him a very good start," they said, "but the end will be the same. She must be very hardhearted and cruel to demand the death of all those she defeats in the races."

Suddenly the signal was given, and a gasp of admiration arose as the figure of Melanion darted forward as swiftly as an arrow from a bow. Swift as he was, however, the sure-footed Atalanta gained on him steadily, and soon he could hear her footsteps close behind him. Without a backward glance, he threw down one of the golden apples which Aphrodite had given him. As soon as Atalanta saw the golden gleam of the apple, sparkling and shimmering in the bright sunshine, she was entranced by its beauty and a great desire came over her to pick it up. This she did, thus enabling the speeding Melanion to gain some distance on her.

Once more, above the pounding of his heart, the brave runner could hear the patter of feet approaching him very swiftly. He waited until the sound was very close and then once again dropped a golden apple. Again the princess stooped to pick it up, and thus gave Melanion a chance to surge forward. When he was quite near the huge tree which was to mark the end of the race, Atalanta was just about to overtake him when he dropped the third apple, and as she slowed her stride to scoop it up, he raced ahead to win.

A great shout of joy arose from the huge crowd, and the hero was led before King Iasus in triumph. He had been anxiously watching the race, for he had taken a liking to the fearless Melanion, and had secretly hoped that by some miracle this bold young man would compel Atalanta to keep her promise. Now it had actually happened, and he smiled happily as the victor was led before him.

"You have won the race against Atalanta, my daughter, and have now the right to claim her as your wife. Do you still wish to marry her? She must keep her promise even though you used a trick in order to defeat her."

"That I do," declared Melanion, "for was I not willing to risk my life for her?"

Now everyone thought that the princess would object because the young man had won the race by means of a trick, and great was their amazement when she said, "I will gladly marry Melanion and keep my promise, for I see that he is noble, clever, and good."

You may be quite sure that a marriage was quickly arranged, and Atalanta loved her husband very dearly indeed. She was never sorry that she had stopped to pick up the golden apples.

The fleet-footed runners are poised for the race,
The host in silence stands,
For many a suitor has lost his life
At the merciless maiden's hands.
A gasp, a sigh, and the two speed by,
The prize—a life and a throne.
An apple drops, the maiden stops,
Melanion runs alone.
Again and again the check and halt,
The victor bounds ahead.
A roar of triumph, the race is o'er,
And each to the king is led.
No more the sound of pounding feet,
No more the race of hate.
The she-bear's ward has met her match,
Rejoices in her fate.

Orpheus and Eurydice

Orpheus, King of Thrace, was a son of the god Apollo, but he was very different from the other Greek heroes. He was indeed very famous, but not because of great deeds in battle. It was because he possessed a wonderful gift. He could play the lyre so beautifully and so cleverly that he could charm anything with his wonderful music.

Even the savage beasts would come running to listen to him, and would stand enthralled as he played. People left their work to flock around him and listen. The very rocks tumbling down the mountainsides would remain still as he sang and plucked the strings of his harp, and the trees would bend their branches as his music cast its spell over all. Even the streams which gushed and tumbled, gurgled and splashed down the mountainsides would cease their clamor and flow more gently into the valley when the silver tones of his voice charmed the very air around him.

Now Orpheus had a wife whose name was Eurydice. She was very beautiful indeed and he loved her very dearly. She loved to listen to the songs he sang and the music he played, and they spent many happy hours together. "No one could be as happy as I am," thought Orpheus as he watched his charming wife seated by his side; and the same thought went through the mind of Eurydice, who was very proud of her husband and his enchanting music.

One day, however, as Eurydice was walking along by the side of a river, she heard footsteps following her. Looking around she saw that Aristaeus, a god who was noted for his wickedness, was pursuing her and meant to do her harm. She began to run as fast as she could to try to escape, and in her haste she did not look where she was going. As her feet trod down the long grass near the river, a snake which had been lying there bit her.

Now Eurydice knew that the snake was a poisonous one and that its bite would certainly cause death. She called loudly for help, but wicked Aristaeus, who had been following her, ran away, and left her to her fate. Poor Eurydice knew that there was nothing she could do to stop her spirit leaving her body and passing away to the Kingdom of Hades, where people went when they died. She lay down on the grass, put down her head, and waited for her spirit to leave her.

When Orpheus discovered that his beautiful Eurydice was dead, he was very sad indeed. "I cannot live upon this earth without my wife," he said. "I will go down to the Kingdom of Hades and plead with King Pluto, who reigns there, to set her spirit free and let me take her back with me."

"You cannot do this," said his friends, "for Pluto will not allow anyone to leave his kingdom. Besides, there are many dangers to be overcome, and the gates of Hades are guarded by the fierce Cerberus, the dog with many heads, whose eyes flame like fire in the darkness of the underworld."

"Nevertheless, I will go," said Orpheus, "for I cannot stay here upon this earth without Eurydice. Better to lose my life in trying to bring her back than live in misery forever."

So Orpheus took his harp and set off on his way to the Kingdom of Hades, from which no man had ever been known to return. First he sacrificed a black ram to the god of the underworld, and then taking an obolos in his hand, he made his way to the river Acheron, which had to be crossed before one could reach the Kingdom of Hades. Now an obolos was a small Greek coin, which the Greeks always placed in the mouths of dead people; and in order to cross the river Acheron, one had to travel in the ferryboat of Charon, the ferryman of the underworld. He would demand an obolos for his trouble, and no one would be taken across who did not have this coin to give. Instead they would be driven away, to wander forever along the deserted shore of the river.

When Orpheus arrived at the ferry, he saw a long black boat in which stood the ancient Charon himself, waiting there in readiness for those who were doomed to cross the river. "Why do you wish to cross the Acheron?" asked Charon. "Know you not that only the spirits of the dead may enter Hades?"

"That I know," replied Orpheus, "but I go to plead with King Pluto to free my wife, Eurydice, and allow her to return with me to earth."

"Think well before you set out," replied Charon, "for once you enter the Kingdom of Pluto, you will not find it possible to return."

"I know the dangers which may befall me, and the risks which I must take," replied Orpheus, "but there can be no life on earth for me without Eurydice."

"Then give me your obolos," said Charon, "for I must not dally too long."

The sorrowing Orpheus gave the ferryman his coin, and after being rowed across the dark gloomy river, soon found himself at the entrance to a long grove of black poplar trees, whose branches intertwined to form a long dark alley. Unafraid, he walked boldly along the grove until he came to a great iron gate which was firmly locked and barred. In front of this gate sat a huge dog with many heads. Its eyes flashed like fire, and at the sight of its many hideous tongues and its terrifying appearance even the brave Orpheus began to lose heart and felt his courage leaving him. When it saw Orpheus, the dog jumped up and began to bark loudly, rushing at him as if it would tear him to pieces.

Then Orpheus took his harp and played on it as he had never played before. The music was sweet and soothing, and at the very first sounds, the dog seemed to lose all its fierceness and listened, enchanted by the wonderful melody. Orpheus played on, and gradually the creature was overcome by the harmonious sounds and lay down at his feet, its heads resting on its paws. Still Orpheus played, and did not stop till he saw that the dog was fast asleep.

To his amazement he noticed that the door which before had been locked and barred had opened by itself, for that too had been enchanted by his music, and the way was now open for him to enter the Kingdom of Hades. He entered a long dark passage and soon found himself in a great hall. At one end of the hall were two thrones. On one of these sat King Pluto, and on the other was his queen, Persephone.

"Who are you?" asked Pluto in a voice which echoed like thunder through the vastness of the hall. "Know you not that living people are not allowed to enter my kingdom? How did you succeed in avoiding my dog Cerberus which guards the gate, and how did you open the gate itself? What folly is this, O mortal, that you dare to brave the anger of Pluto?"

Orpheus looked at the stern gray face of the king, but made no reply. He took his harp and began to play such music as

Then Orpheus took his harp and played on it as he had never played before

no one had ever heard. His very heart and all his love for Eurydice seemed to enter into the harp strings, and the sweet melody which he created softened the cold heart of Pluto. Great tears of bronze rolled down his stern cheeks, and there was a softness in his voice when he said, "What is your wish? Ask of me what you desire and I will grant it, for none would dare enter my kingdom unless they desired something more precious than their own lives. Ask, O musician of enchantment, for your music stirs my soul to pity."

Orpheus ceased his playing and said, "O Pluto, mighty King of the Underworld, grant me this boon. Let me have again my beloved wife, Eurydice, who is doomed to dwell here among the shades. Grant that I may take her back with me to the earth, where we lived in such happiness. To you she is only one subject among many, but to me she means more than life itself. Let me take her back to the sunshine, the blue skies, and the green fields; back to the song of the birds and the laughter of the gurgling mountain streams."

"Your wish is granted," replied the king. "You may take her back with you, but you must obey me in all that I command. You will go first and Eurydice will follow. You must possess yourself in patience until you have reached the earth once again. If you turn around to look back, if you look even once, she will have to return to my kingdom forever. Trust me to keep my promise, and she will surely follow you to earth; but remember if you look back at all, she will be lost to you forever, and will return to dwell in sorrow and darkness."

Orpheus took his harp and played sweet music as he left the throne of Pluto. On he went through the hall, along the dark passage, till he came to the grove of black poplars. Still he played, not once looking back for fear of losing Eurydice. However, he could not help doubting that his wish had come true, and he longed to take just one little peep over his shoulder to see if she were indeed following him.

As he reached the shore of the great black river, the temptation to look back was too great for him to overcome. He could bear the strain no longer and he turned quickly around to see if Eurydice were really following him. As he looked, he saw her behind him, pale and faint in the half-light, but even as he looked, her figure began to disappear from sight.

He heard her voice, however, sad and mournful. "Oh, my husband!" she said. "Why did you look back? I had almost reached the earth again and could picture the gay flowers of the meadow and the sweet kiss of the sunshine. Why did you look back? Now I must dwell in the Kingdom of the Shades forever." Her voice became faint, like the whisper of a soft wind amongst the reeds by the river, and was heard no more.

When Orpheus realized what he had done, he sat down and wept bitterly. He did not care to return alone to the earth which held no happiness for him without his beloved wife. His heart was broken. People say that he did not even cross the river, but lay down on the ground until his spirit departed from him and went to join Eurydice's in the Kingdom of the Underworld.

When the soft winds blow through the poplar trees
And the lambkins frisk on the hill,
When the birds in flight sing hymns to the light
And the water laughs in the rill,
What melody haunts the grassy slopes,
Enchants the woodland glades?
What lilting tune do the breezes croon
As they stir the verdant shades?
Are they the songs that Orpheus sang
When his heart was happy and free,
When he plucked the strings of his magic harp
For sweet Eurydice?

Theseus and Ariadne

Aegeus, King of Athens, was very unhappy when he found
that he had to return suddenly to his kingdom.

He had been staying with his queen, Aethra, at the home of
her father, and he knew that very shortly a child would be
born to them. News came, however, that there was great
trouble in Athens and that he had to return without delay.

"I must go back to my country," he said to Aethra, "and
I will be away for some years. Before I go, I will place my

sword and my sandals beneath the great rock near your father's palace. If a male child is born, you must call him Theseus, and when he is old enough, you must tell him of the sword and sandals. When he is strong enough to move the rock and find these things, you must ask him to do so, and bring them to me in Athens. Then I will acknowledge him as my son, and he shall help me to rule my kingdom."

A little boy was indeed born to Aethra, and when he was sixteen years old, she told him what his father had commanded. Theseus, as he was now called, lost no time in finding the huge rock, which he moved quite easily, in spite of its tremendous size and weight. There he found the sword and sandals, and immediately set off for Athens to make himself known to his father.

He had many adventures before he arrived in his father's kingdom and became a bold and daring champion of those in distress. Great was the joy of Aegeus when he recognized the sword and sandals which Theseus was carrying. "Welcome to my kingdom," he said, "for never was I in greater need of help than I am now. I am told that you are a skilled and mighty warrior, and I am proud to have such a son as you to help me rule my country."

"I set off as soon as my mother had told me of your wish," replied the happy Theseus, "and now I wish to stay in Athens and help you to fight against your enemies."

"Alas, my son!" said Aegeus. "This country has fallen upon very sad times indeed. We have been plagued by famine and disease, and have even been defeated in battle by Minos, the King of Crete. Even the gods seem to have deserted us, and I have been forced to ask for peace, for we could not withstand the fierce attacks made upon us by the cruel Minos and his warriors."

"But that is over now, my father," said Theseus, "and I am here to help you. Surely we can now defeat all your enemies."

"That is bravely spoken, my son," said the king, "but I have not yet told you everything. When Minos agreed to cease his attacks upon Athens, it was because I had promised to send a tribute to him every nine years. I had to agree to send him seven youths and seven maidens. When these youths and maidens arrive in Crete they are taken to a cave full of winding passages so that they cannot find their way out.

"Within this maze of passages lives a dreadful monster called the Minotaur. He has the head of a bull and the body of a very powerful man. He is a most terrifying monster who knows no mercy. When he finds the youths and maidens wandering helplessly about, he kills and devours them. Alas that this great sorrow has fallen upon us! The might of Athens is now a dream of the past, and there is no one to help us in our distress."

"I am not afraid of any monster," said Theseus. "Did I not capture the wild bull of Athia and sacrifice him to Apollo? Did I not slay the giant Polyphemon and the wicked bandit Periphetes? Many were the monsters I overcame before I arrived in Athens."

"I have heard of these adventures," replied his father, "but the Minotaur is more difficult to overcome, for he lives in the darkness of the labyrinth of passages, and comes upon his victims unaware. Besides, you would have to go as one of the seven youths who are sent as tribute, and who knows what the cruel Minos would do if he found out that you were my son!"

"Let me go with the youths and maidens to Crete," pleaded Theseus. "I will surely rid the world of this monster and will return to you unharmed."

"I fear to let you do this, my son, even though you are so bold and fearless," replied the king, "but perhaps the gods will help you, and bring peace to Athens once again. When the time comes I will send you with the others, but take care that Minos does not discover who you are."

Now when the time arrived for the next group of young people to be taken to Crete, Theseus sailed with them. Before he left, however, he said to his father, "If I am successful in slaying this monster and return in safety, you will know in advance of my success. The ship on which I return will be carrying a white sail, and that will be a sign of my safety and that all is well. If, however, you see a black sail, you will know that I shall never return. Keep watch for the home-coming ship, and let prayers be offered to the gods for the success of my venture."

Now as the ship approached the island of Crete, its mournful black sail flapping in the wind, a great crowd of people came to watch the unfortunate victims being brought ashore.

Among those who watched was Ariadne, the beautiful daughter of King Minos. She noticed that while the other youths and maidens wept and mourned, one of them looked brave and cheerful, and stared boldly about him. She noticed his strong, supple figure and his handsome face.

"This one has the bearing of a prince," she said to herself. "I must find a way to save him from the dreadful fate which befalls all the poor victims who are thrust into the cave."

That night, as the youths and maidens lay chained in prison ready for the next day, when they would be taken to the labyrinth, Ariadne came to Theseus and gave him a ball of thread. "Take this with you," she said, "and fasten one end of it to the entrance of the cave. Unwind it as you go along the passages and you will then be able to find your way out. Take also this sharp sword, which you must use to fight the Minotaur."

"Who are you," asked Theseus, "and why do you seek to help me?"

"I am Ariadne, the daughter of King Minos," she replied, "and I have no love for the cruel deeds of my father. I must not stay any longer, however, for if my father finds out, he will be very angry indeed, and might think of even more cruel things to do. I will wait for you tomorrow at the entrance to the cave, and pray for your success."

Next day the young victims were led to the labyrinth, and left to their fate. "Fear not!" said Theseus to his companions. "Do not move from this spot. I will go in search of the Minotaur. Hold fast to the end of this thread, and I will unwind it as I go along. Hold it firmly and it will guide me back to you and the entrance of the cave."

Fearlessly he set forth through the dark twisting passages, unwinding the thread as he moved along. Soon he could hear the bellowing of the dreaded monster in the distance, and he seized the sword which Ariadne had given him. Nearer and nearer came the roars of the evil monster, and before long Theseus could make out the form of a huge giant with the face of a bull approaching him. Although the body was that of a man, the hands were like hideous talons, held out in readiness to grasp and tear his victims to pieces.

The bold hero did not hesitate, but sprang forward as the Minotaur approached him, and with a mighty thrust of the sharp sword slew the dreaded monster. Then, guided by the thread, he made his way back to his companions, who had been waiting in terror near the mouth of the cave.

"Let us wait until nightfall," he said, "and then we will make our way down to the ship. In the darkness it will be easy for us to escape, and we can return safely to our homes in Athens." They waited patiently until the faint glimmer at the mouth of the cave had gone and they knew that it was night. Then they made their way out onto the hill slope overlooking the bay where the black-sailed ship was gently riding the waves of the incoming tide. There Ariadne was waiting for them, just as she had promised.

"Take me with you," she said to Theseus, "for I long to leave the home of my cruel father, and I would like to go to Athens with you."

The bold hero did not hesitate, but sprang
forward as the Minotaur approached him

"That I will gladly do," said Theseus, "and if you will agree to marry me, I will make you proud and happy, for you have saved the life of none other than Theseus, son of Aegeus, King of Athens."

"I will gladly be your wife," replied Ariadne, "but now we must hurry, lest our escape is discovered."

Happily the young people all made their way to the ship, and set sail for Greece. Now it was quite a long journey, and after they had sailed for some days, they came to an island, and, as it was night, they decided to go on shore and sleep there.

That night, as Theseus slept, the god Dionysus appeared to him in his dream. "Theseus, son of Aegeus," said the god, "I have come to warn you that you must not take Ariadne back with you to Greece. She has been chosen as a wife for me, for I love her dearly, and she must be left on this island. No harm will befall her, and in time she will forget you and be quite happy; but do not disobey me, O Theseus, if you wish to reach your father's home in safety."

Now the young hero was very sad at heart when he heard this, but he dared not disobey a god. Sorrowfully he arose and quietly waking his companions, they set sail, leaving the sleeping Ariadne behind.

Next morning when the maiden awoke, she found to her great distress that the island was deserted. All the young people had gone, and the only echo to her cries of despair was the call of the sea birds as they flew overhead. She ran down to the blue water and in the distance she could just make out the faint outlines of the ship now quite a long distance off.

"Come back, O Theseus!" she cried. "Why have you left me alone on this island? Come back! Come back!" But Theseus could not hear her cries, nor did he even look back upon the island, for his heart, too, was very sad, and he feared that if he looked back he might be tempted to return.

As Ariadne sat down by the water's edge, weeping and lamenting her fate, she suddenly heard the sound of music and laughter, and there coming towards her was a large number of men and women. Leading the procession was a golden chariot in which rode the most handsome man she had ever seen. He was dressed in the skin of a leopard and round his head was a wreath of vine leaves. He seemed to be surrounded by a bright light, and Ariadne forgot her sorrow at this wonderful sight.

The procession stopped, and the youth, who was no other than the god Dionysus, spoke to her. "O beautiful maiden," he said, "mourn not for the loss of Theseus, for he has departed at my command. I am the god Dionysus, and I have come to take you as my bride. No longer will you be a mortal, for I will take you to live with me among the gods on Mount Olympus. There you will live in eternal happiness, for as the wife of a god you will never die. Come with me, Ariadne, and forget your sorrow."

The daughter of Minos looked upon the handsome Dionysus and a feeling of great happiness came over her. "I will go with you," she said, and stepping onto the chariot, she was carried amid great rejoicing to the top of Mount Olympus.

As for Theseus, however, he was distressed for quite a long time, but as his ship approached the shores of Greece, he began to think of the excitement of bringing back his companions in safety and the welcome that awaited them all in Athens. In his excitement he forgot to change the black sail to a white one, as he had arranged with his father.

Now when Aegeus heard that a ship was approaching, he made his way to the top of a cliff to see if it could be the ship of his son returning successfully from his adventure in Crete. Seeing the black sail, he believed that Theseus had been devoured by the monster. He was filled with despair at the thought of having lost the son he loved so much, and climbing up to the top of the cliff, he threw himself down into the sea and was killed.

Theseus mourned his death for many weeks, and vowed that he would rule as nobly in his stead as his father would have wished him to do.

This indeed he did, and the Kingdom of Attica became a powerful and united kingdom.

During his reign the people were very happy and many buildings and temples were erected. When Theseus died, his body was placed in the sacred enclosure of Theseum, the remains of which can be seen to this very day.

The Adventures of Perseus

There was once a very wicked king of Argos who was named Acrisius. This king had been told that when his daughter Danae married, she would have a son who would bring about his death. "I will imprison my daughter, so that she cannot marry," said Acrisius, "and then I shall have nothing to fear." He caused a huge underground chamber to be built of bronze and into this poor Danae was cast.

The king, however, was not to have his way, for one day the god Zeus appeared to Danae and told her that a son would be born to her, and that he should be named Perseus. The words of Zeus came true, and when Acrisius heard of the birth of the little boy, he was both angry and afraid. He obtained a huge wooden chest and shut up both mother and child inside it. Then he made his servants take the chest down to the sea, where it was carried away by the waves.

The huge chest was tossed up and down by the waves for many days, and at last was cast up on the shore of the island of Seriphos. Here a fisherman named Dictys saw it as he was casting his nets. Great was his astonishment when he opened the chest and saw Danae and her baby inside. When she told him her story, he was full of pity for her. "I will take you to my brother Polydectes," he said, "for he is king of this island and will protect you from your wicked father, who seeks to make an end of both you and his grandchild."

Some years went by, and Perseus grew up to be a very strong and handsome young man, being as brave as he was beautiful. Now Polydectes fell in love with Danae, and wanted to marry her, but she would not agree to marry him. He knew that as king of that country he could compel Danae to do as he wished, but he was afraid of the anger of Perseus, whose fearless courage was now well known.

"I will find some task for him to do," said Polydectes, "some dangerous task which I know will bring about his death. Then I shall have no cause to fear him." He sent for Perseus and said, "I have heard of your strength and bravery, and in return for saving your mother's life and your own, I wish you to perform a very dangerous task for me."

"Tell me what you desire," said Perseus, who had no idea of the evil that was in the heart of the king. "Speak, O Polydectes, and I will try to carry out your wish."

"Far across the sea, at the other side of the world," said the king, "is the Gorgon Medusa. Your task is to cut off her head and bring it back to me."

"That I will gladly do," replied Perseus, "for I cannot refuse a gift to one who has protected me from my wicked grandfather."

"I must warn you," said Polydectes, "that the task you have undertaken is no easy one. The Gorgon Medusa is one of three sisters, all dreadful monsters and fearful to look upon. They have teeth like the tusks of the wild boar, and golden wings. Their hands are clawlike and made of brass, while instead of hair each has a mass of wriggling, hissing, poisonous snakes. None may look at the face of Medusa, for if they do, they are instantly turned to stone."

"I am not afraid," said Perseus. "I will carry out the task you have set me." He said good-by to his mother, and started off on his dangerous mission, much to the delight of Polydectes, who thought he would never see him again.

Now Perseus travelled a very long way, and then feeling tired, he lay down and fell into a deep sleep. In his sleep there appeared before him the goddess Athene, who said, "Perseus, you have set yourself a most dangerous task which no ordinary mortal could hope to perform. However, my father, the god Zeus, has sent me to help you and to tell you what to do. When you awake, you will find a bronze mirror by your side. This you must use when you find the Gorgon Medusa, for you cannot look upon her face without it, lest you be changed to stone. When you reach her, you must look in the mirror and strike off her head."

When Perseus awoke, he did indeed find the bronze mirror lying at his side, and he felt very happy that the gods had decided to help him. On he went again, over fields and valleys, mountains and hills, till again he lay down to rest. No sooner had he fallen asleep, however, than he saw in a vision the god Hermes standing before him. He was wearing a pair of golden sandals, fastened to each of which was a small pair of wings. These sandals were magic and could carry him over land and sea very swiftly indeed.

"I am the god Hermes," he said, "and I, too, have been sent to help you in your task, for the gods look kindly upon you, and wish you to be successful in what you have undertaken. I have brought you a sword which nothing can withstand. You will find it by your side when you awake. Now the gods have helped you all they can, but there are others who can help you too. When you awake, you must look about you and you will see a huge mountain in the distance. This you must climb, and when you have descended the other side, you will come to a cave.

"This is a very gloomy cave, and in it live the three Gray Sisters. Now remember, O Perseus, that these sisters are relations of the Gorgons, and will not help you until you force them to do so. They have only one eye and one tooth among the three of them. These you must seize and refuse to return, until they have told you the way to go. You must have no mercy for them, for they are as cunning as they are old and ugly, and will try to deceive you so as to lead you into danger. Farewell, O Perseus, beloved of the gods."

In the morning Perseus found the magic sword by his side and felt more encouraged than ever. He looked about him, and there in the distance he could see a huge mountain whose peak seemed to reach into the sky. It was further off than he had thought and he was very tired indeed when at last he found himself scrambling down the other side. Soon he found the cave which Hermes had told him about, and he entered it very quietly.

There on the ground were the three ugly old hags known as the three Gray Sisters. They were huddled up fast asleep, and their tooth and eye lay on the ground near them. As he approached, they awoke and one of them put out her hand to take the eye and see who was there. Perseus, however, darted forward like an arrow from a bow, and seized both the eye and the tooth.

"Give them back to us!" screamed the old hags. "Give them back at once, or we will cast a spell over you."

"That you cannot do," laughed Perseus, "for without your eye and tooth you are powerless to do anything. I will not give them back to you until you tell me the way to the home of Medusa, the Gorgon."

The ugly old sisters stood up and blundered about the cave trying to grasp the eye, but the hero was easily able to avoid them, for without the eye they were quite blind.

"Be still," said Perseus, "and tell me what I want to know, or you will never get back your eye and tooth, and I will cut off your heads with my sword. If you tell me where to find the home of Medusa, I will give them back to you and no harm will befall you."

Seeing that they would have to obey him, the three Gray Sisters said, "The home of the Gorgons is hidden from us, but this we can tell you. Hasten to the shore of the great ocean where dwell the water nymphs. They know where the Gorgons dwell, and they will help you. Now give us back our eye and tooth."

Now Perseus, seeing that the old hags had told him all they knew, gave them back the eye and tooth, and set off for the shore of the great ocean. He travelled for many days, until at last he reached the sandy shore, where the waves came tumbling towards him, and the white foam splashed and gleamed in the sunlight.

He stood for a moment gazing over the wide ocean and then he called out: "O nymphs of the ocean, hearken to the voice of Perseus who asks your help in the name of Zeus himself." He had no sooner uttered the words than a number of water nymphs rose up from the waves and came towards him.

"What do you require, O daring one who speaks in the name of the gods?" they asked. "How can we help?"

"I seek to find the home of the Gorgon Medusa," replied Perseus, "that I may slay her and take her head back with me to the island of Seriphos."

"You will find Medusa and the other Gorgons on a small rocky island in the middle of the ocean," they replied. "It will be no easy task even to approach the island, for the horrid creatures have snakes instead of hair, which hiss and give warning when anyone approaches. However, it is their custom to sleep when the sun is hot at noonday, and that is the time to approach. Even then, if you succeed in slaying Medusa, the others will attack and destroy you immediately unless you are aided by the immortals. We will give you three gifts which will help you. The first is a pair of sandals which will enable you to fly through the air at great speed, so that you will be able to approach and escape quickly. The second gift is a magic helmet which makes its wearer invisible, and then the ever-watchful snakes will not see you, nor will the other Gorgons know where to pursue you. The third gift is a bag in which you must put the Gorgon's head immediately you have it cut off, for to look at it means certain death, since you will be changed immediately to stone. Go now, for noon is fast approaching, and soon the Gorgons will be asleep."

Perseus thanked the nymphs for their gifts, and putting on the sandals, flew swiftly over the waves until he came to a rocky island in the middle of the ocean. Here was the dwelling of the Gorgons, and as he peered about him, he saw a cave and heard the sound of breathing. He put on his helmet which made him invisible, and holding up the bronze mirror which

Athene had given him, he entered the cave backwards, looking steadily into the mirror all the time. Seizing the sword of Hermes, he struck swiftly at the head of Medusa and cut it off. Still looking into the mirror, he placed the head in the bag which the nymphs had given him, and sped swiftly out of the cave.

The other Gorgons by now were awake, and seeing that their sister was dead, they rushed after Perseus, screaming, clawing, and hissing as they went. They could not catch him, however, for his magic helmet made him invisible and his sandals bore him swiftly away so that the horrible creatures were left clawing angrily at the air.

Now Perseus flew on until he came to a country called Ethiopia, which is part of Africa. The people of this country were in great trouble because their king had quarrelled with the sea-god Poseidon, who in his anger had sent a dreadful dragon to attack them. This terrible monster came up out of the sea and destroyed the land and the people wherever he went.

In despair, the king had asked his priests what he should do to save his country from the attacks of this cruel monster. "What can I do to save my country?" he said, "for this dragon has already destroyed much cattle and eaten many people. Each time he comes he causes much sorrow and weeping, and I am in great distress. Is there no way by which I can cause the monster to cease his attacks upon us?"

"There is only one way," said the priests, "and that we fear to tell you, for it will bring you great sorrow."

"Speak," said the king, "for no matter what sorrow it causes me, I must save my country and my people."

"Then," said the priests, "the only way to bring peace again to our country is to give your only daughter, Andromeda, to the dragon to be devoured."

Now Andromeda was young and beautiful, and the king loved her dearly, but he was willing to give her to the dragon if it would save the rest of the people. The poor maiden was taken, therefore, and chained to a rock on the seashore to await the coming of the monster.

When Perseus was approaching the shore, he saw the weeping form of Andromeda chained to the rock. "What is the cause of your weeping?" he asked. "And why have you been chained to the rock?"

"I am Andromeda, daughter of the king of Ethiopia," she replied, "and I have been fastened here as a sacrifice to the dreadful dragon which has ravaged our country. Soon he will come and devour me, for only in this way can our country be saved."

"The dragon will not devour you," said Perseus, "for I will wait here with you and slay him when he approaches."

"That you cannot do," wept Andromeda, "for no man can overcome the monster. Go away quickly, for he will soon come, and if you try to protect me, he will devour you too."

"Not so," said the hero, "for I am Perseus. I wear the winged sandals and carry the sword of Hermes, which never misses its stroke. Weep no more, O maiden, for I will fight the dragon and put an end to the sorrows of your father."

Even as he spoke, the waters of the ocean were disturbed and began to foam and boil. Suddenly, the head of the dragon rose above the waves, and Andromeda watched it in terror as it approached, making great waves as it sped towards her. Then Perseus grasped his sword and flew down upon it. Again and again he slashed at its neck, while the dragon opened wide its great jaws and lashed its tail in terrible anger. Still Perseus slashed away, and after one last mighty swish with its tail, the dreadful creature ceased its struggle and sank dead beneath the water of the red-stained sea.

You can imagine how happy the king was to have Andromeda back, and to know that the dragon was dead. "Ask of me what you desire," he said to Perseus, "and if it is at all in my power, I will grant it to you."

"I have saved the life of your only daughter," replied Perseus, "and now I ask your permission to marry her, and take her to my home on the island of Seriphos."

"That I will gladly give," said the king, "for I could not desire a nobler husband for my daughter than the mighty Perseus, beloved of the gods."

So Perseus and Andromeda were married, and together they left her father's kingdom to go to the island where the hero hoped to find his mother happy and well. When at last they arrived, Perseus found that his mother was being ill-treated by King Polydectes. He had asked her many times to marry him, but she had continually refused, and in his thwarted anger he had ordered that she should be imprisoned in a room and given no food. He hoped in this way that at last she would be forced to agree to marry him.

When Polydectes saw Perseus, he was very much afraid, for he had fully believed that the young man would never return. In a fit of anger he seized a sword and tried to kill him.

Perseus, however, took the head of the Gorgon Medusa out of the bag and held it up in front of Polydectes, while he turned his head away. Immediately the wicked king was turned to stone, and Perseus knew that his mother was now safe from any harm.

Still the adventures of Perseus were not at an end. The prophecy of the gods had still to be fulfilled, and the hero and his mother left Seriphos to sail to the land of Argos, where his grandfather Acrisius still lived. You can imagine the terror of the heartless king when he saw his daughter Danae and her son returning after such a long time. He tried in vain to avoid the fate which had been foretold to him before his grandson had been born. One day, during a game of discus throwing which Acrisius had been watching, Perseus threw a discus which missed its mark and struck the king instead, causing him to be killed instantly. Thus did the words of the gods come true.

Perseus, however, did not remain in Argos, for he did not wish to be king in that land. We are told that he journeyed over the sea to Mycenae, where he reigned for many years until his death.

The Legend of Arachne

We have all seen a spider, that wonderful and patient weaver of webs, which is to be found in the grandest castle and the humblest cottage.

In autumn time we see the spider's web upon the branches of trees, looking like a fairy network with the dewdrops glistening upon it. This is one of nature's marvels, and most peoples of the world have some story to tell about how these patient creatures came into being.

This is the story told by the ancient Greeks:

The goddess Athene, daughter of the great Zeus, was perhaps the most gifted of all the Greek gods and goddesses. She it was who taught the people of Cyrene how to tame horses and use them for their daily needs. She taught the warriors how to make and use the first war chariots. The humble potter at his wheel blessed her for the skill she had given him. Above all, however, the great goddess was famed for her wonderful knowledge of weaving cloth and decorating it with beautiful embroidery.

Whenever a Greek maiden showed more skill than others at weaving patterns, people would say, "She has the blessing of Athene."

Now in the city of Colophon in Lydia, there lived a man named Idmon. He was a dyer, famous throughout the whole of Lydia for his knowledge of how to make the very costly purple dye, and because of his knowledge and skill, he had become very rich indeed. In spite of his riches, however, he was very unhappy because he had no child of his own.

Idmon loved children, and often sighed at his work when he thought of his neighbor's children. "If only the gods would grant me this blessing," he sighed, "I would be the happiest man in Lydia." Then he would try to forget his sorrow by working even harder at making the most lovely purple cloth in the kingdom.

Athene was very touched at his great sorrow, and because

of his great skill, and noble character, she decided to grant his dearest wish. One day, as he was busy at his work, he had a strange feeling that he was being watched, and looking up, he saw before him the most beautiful lady he had ever seen in all his life. She wore a long flowing gown of delicately-embroidered cloth, the patterns on which seemed to glow with a strange light. On her head was a crown of pure gold, and in her hand was a long golden wand upon which strange figures were carved. She had a look of great tenderness and pity in her eyes, and though Idmon was for a moment startled, he was not afraid.

"Surely thou art the goddess Athene herself," he exclaimed, "for none other could be so graceful and so beautiful."

"I am indeed Athene," replied the goddess, "and I know the great sorrow that is in thy heart, O Idmon. I have watched thee at thy work, and have admired thy skill and thy humble heart. It is for this reason that I have come to grant thy wish. The day will come when thou wilt be the father of a beautiful daughter, who will be as skilful at weaving as she will be famed for her beauty.

"Beware, however, that thou dost not allow her to become vain and conceited, for then I will remove my blessing from her, and an evil fate will befall her. Take heed, O Idmon, teach her well, and make sure that she possesses the same humbleness of heart as thou hast thyself."

As she finished speaking, the goddess disappeared, and Idmon could not believe that he had seen Athene standing before him. Yet her words seemed to echo in his mind over and over again, and a feeling of great happiness came over him.

Many months went by, and then one day the words of the goddess came true. A beautiful baby girl was born, and the happiness of Idmon knew no bounds. "We will call our daughter Arachne," he said to his wife, "and we must heed the words of Athene. Let us at all times teach her to be humble, for that is the wish of the goddess."

You may be quite sure that Idmon was as good as his word. Arachne grew up to be a beautiful maiden, rivalling the fairest in the land with her beauty. Under the skilful guidance of Athene, her skill as a weaver and embroiderer became as famous as her beauty. She could handle the needle and spindle in a way that no other woman in the country could ever hope to do. She wove such wonderful patterns and scenes that people came from far and wide to see her work. She became so famous for her spinning and weaving that when people wished to describe something pretty they would say, "As beautiful as the embroidery of Arachne."

Of course her parents were very proud of her. It would indeed have been very strange if they had not been. Yet a great fear entered their hearts lest Arachne should become vain and boastful, and so bring upon herself the evil which Athene had foretold. Whenever she had embroidered some beautiful pattern, they would say, "Yes, it is very pretty, but you have still very much to learn." In this way they hoped to make the girl less boastful, and so avoid the anger of the goddess.

In spite of all their efforts, however, the constant praises of the people who came to admire her work did cause Arachne to think a great deal of her skill. Gradually she became so vain that she dared to boast that her embroidery was better than even that of Athene herself. "If Athene appeared before me now," she would say, "I would challenge her to weave more skilful and more beautiful patterns than I can, for I know that there is no one to rival me in all the world."

You can well imagine how sad and fearful were the parents of Arachne when they heard the vain boastful words of the foolish girl. "You must not speak in this manner," they said, "for who can rival the goddess who taught the world the arts of spinning and weaving? Cease your boasting and foolish talk, less evil befall you and you bring sorrow upon those who love you."

"It is not foolish talk," said Arachne angrily, "I am indeed the finest embroiderer in the world. I do not care if Athene does hear me, for what I say is true."

"Still thy vain tongue," said the grief-stricken Idmon, who was by now very much alarmed. He remembered the warning of the goddess. The words she had spoken echoed in his mind. "Beware that thou dost not allow her to become vain and conceited, for then I will remove my blessing from her, and an evil fate will befall her."

When Athene heard Arachne's words, she was sorry, for she did not wish to hurt the humble Idmon and his wife. She knew that if she kept her promise to punish Arachne for her boastfulness, it would break their hearts. She therefore decided to warn the girl, in the hope that a warning from a stranger would be sufficient to cure her.

One day, just as Arachne was showing off her work to an admiring crowd of friends, and boasting as usual of her skill, Athene appeared before her, disguised as a poor old woman. "Boastful creature," said the old woman, "do you indeed think that you can spin and weave as well as the goddess Athene? Your work may seem beautiful to your eyes, and those of your friends, but none can rival the embroidery of the goddess who taught the world the art of the needle and spindle. Do not deceive yourself, and watch the utterances of your vain, conceited tongue, lest you rouse Athene to anger, and bring upon yourself the punishment your boasting so richly deserves."

"Begone, old hag," replied Arachne scornfully, driven to anger by the words of the old woman. "What can you know of the art of embroidery, or what Athene can do, or cannot do? I say again that if the goddess were here amongst us, I would challenge her to a contest, and I know who would weave the better patterns and designs."

At these vain words, Athene could no longer contain her anger, and she decided to show herself in her true form. There was a flash of light, and a warm glow filled the air. There before the startled gaze of the assembled crowd stood Athene in all her glory. "It is indeed Athene to whom you speak," said the goddess to the boastful maiden, who could not believe her eyes when she saw the sudden change in the old woman to whom she had been speaking. "It is indeed Athene," repeated the goddess, "and to teach you a lesson in humility,

Athene appeared before her, disguised as a poor old woman

I am going to accept your challenge."

As she spoke, she waved the golden wand in her hand, and to the amazement of all, there appeared a spindle and frame, such as was used for embroidering cloth. "Now," said Athene, "let us each begin to embroider patterns, and when we have completed them, we will compare them and see which are the better."

You can well imagine the breathless excitement of the watching crowd as Arachne and Athene began their work. The looms were set up, and the threads were tightened in the form of a network. Then the competition began. Arachne guided her shuttle through the tight network with all the skill she possessed. She chose for her design scenes in the lives of the gods who dwelt on Mount Olympus, and so wonderful was her work that gasps of admiration came from the excited spectators.

Athene was indeed hard put to it to keep up with the flying shuttle of Arachne, yet as the contest went on, it could easily be seen that the designs of Athene were even more thrilling and exciting than those of her competitor.

When the contest was over, there was no doubt at all that the work of Athene was the better. Arachne, realizing that she had done her best and yet was no match for the goddess, hung her head in shame. Gone was her boastful manner and vain words, but she had learned her lesson too late. She had tried the patience of Athene once too often.

"Foolish creature," said the angry goddess, "let this lesson be ever in your heart. No more will you boast that you are more skilful than the goddess who brought the art of weaving into the world."

In her anger, Athene tore to shreds the work of Arachne, who rose and fled weeping from the scene. In the quiet of her room, the downcast maiden wept as if her heart would break. She felt that she could no longer hold up her head, for she had been put to shame before all her friends. "I cannot face my friends again," she sobbed. "It would be far better for me if I did not live to see the light of the approaching dawn." In her despair, she tried to hang herself by placing her head through a loop in a rope which was hanging from the ceiling.

Athene, however, would not let the wretched girl end her life in this way. Just as Arachne was on the point of death, the goddess loosened the rope, and the hapless maiden opened her eyes to see Athene standing before her.

"This is not the punishment I have decided upon for you," said the goddess. "There is no doubt about your skill in weaving, and since you have been so fond of boasting about it, you shall weave forever. Your name shall indeed be Arachne, the spider, and your home will be in the threads you weave, in the darkest corners of a room."

She raised her golden wand, and a horrible change came over the girl. The body of Arachne shrank and shrank, and gradually took on the form of a spider. The rope became a spider's web hanging from the ceiling, and the newly-formed spider scuttled away to the center of the web to hide in shame.

That, says the legend, is how the first spider came into the world.

Little creature of the night,
Hiding from the sun's bright light,
Working ever in the gloom,
Setting up your silken loom,
Weaving in a wondrous way,
Once you wove by light of day.
Once you wove with threads of gold,
Scarlet, purple, patterns bold,
Scenes from Mount Olympus' height,
Glowing with a lustre bright.
Now your heart must ever grieve
As your lonely web you weave.
Vanity was not the way
Athene's kindness to repay.

The Legend of Cadmus and Europa

Many years ago, in the far-off country of Phoenicia, lived a brother and sister named Cadmus and Europa. Their father was dead, but their mother, Telephassa, loved them very dearly indeed. Their home was in a very beautiful valley, in which grew all kinds of delicious fruits and sweet-scented flowers. Many a happy day they spent playing by the side of a wide river which flowed past their home.

As the years went by, Europa grew into a very beautiful maiden, and the god Zeus fell in love with her and wished to marry her. He knew, however, that Cadmus guarded his sister jealously and would not allow anyone to approach her. He therefore decided to carry her away by a trick.

One day, as the two young people were watching their mother's cattle in the field, they suddenly noticed a beautiful white bull standing quite still among the other animals. He was as white as pure snow, without a speck of any other color on any part of his body. The bull looked at them with large, gentle eyes, and seemed to invite them to come and play with him.

He looked so gentle that they went nearer and nearer to him, and then, when they were near enough, they began to stroke him and pat him. The bull rubbed his face gently against Europa, and then knelt down, as if inviting her to climb onto his back. By this time Europa had lost any fear she might have had and boldly clambered onto the back of the gentle-looking creature. Slowly the bull rose up from the ground, and carried the laughing maiden round and round the field.

At first Cadmus walked by her side to make sure that no harm befell her, but gradually he allowed the bull to stray alone towards the bank of the river. "It is quite safe," he thought to himself. "The bull is tame, and no harm will befall my sister." To his dismay, however, the bull suddenly began to move very quickly indeed, and Cadmus pursued it, shouting after it, in an attempt to stop it.

His efforts were all in vain, however, for soon the creature was running with the speed of the wind. Across the river he sped, and over a wide grassy plain to the seashore. With a bound he sprang into the waves, carrying the now weeping maiden with him. Cadmus watched helplessly, until the bull was a mere white speck in the distance, at last disappearing from view.

You can imagine how sad Cadmus was when he saw his sister being carried away from him in this mysterious manner. He stood on the seashore, hoping that the bull would return, carrying Europa with him, but he waited in vain. The sun set, and as night approached, the weeping Cadmus knew that he must return home without his beloved sister. The poor youth sobbed bitterly. "What am I going to say to my mother?" he wailed. "A fine guardian I have proved myself to be. This will break my mother's heart."

When Telephassa saw her son returning without Europa, she was filled with alarm, and ran to meet him. "Where is Europa?" she cried. "What has happened that you return alone?" Between his sobs, Cadmus told her what had happened, and poor Telephassa was filled with grief and sorrow for her lost daughter. "We must go in search of her," she cried, "and we will never give up until she is found."

"I am partly to blame, Mother," said Cadmus, "for I should never have allowed Europa to get onto the back of the treacherous creature. I, too, vow that I will never give up the search till my beloved sister is found."

Mother and son waited for the first signs of approaching day with growing impatience, and while the stars could still be seen in the pale light of dawn, they set off on their quest for Europa. At first they travelled quickly, following the wide

river to the grassy plains, and down to the seashore. They wandered along the shore for a long time, until they found a part where the sea narrowed to a strait. Here a boatman offered to take them across. They asked him if he had seen a white bull carrying a maiden on his back, but their question was in vain. He had not seen the creature, nor could he help them except by taking them across the sea.

When they reached the other shore, they found that before long they were confronted by high mountains and rocky hills. They trudged and climbed, trudged and climbed, until Telephassa could no longer drag her weary feet. "We will spend the night here," said Cadmus, who was indeed very weary himself, "and tomorrow we will continue the search."

"No, my son," replied his mother, "we must go on and on, no matter how weary we are, for as the time passes, the chances of finding Europa grow less and less."

"We cannot travel in this strange, forbidding country during the hours of darkness," replied Cadmus. "It is foolish to do so, for we may be going in the wrong direction, and all our efforts will have been in vain."

"You speak words of wisdom," said the anguished mother, "though I would go on if I could compel my feet to do so."

In this way was Telephassa persuaded to spend the night in a deep valley between the gloomy, towering mountains.

Next day, as soon as it was light enough to see, they continued their weary journey, until after many hours, they found themselves descending the mountain slopes towards the sunny plains of Thessaly. Here they saw farm workers busy at their tasks, and asked each one if he had seen the white bull with a girl on its back. Each one gave the same disappointing reply: "We have not seen such a creature," they said, "nor can we believe that such an animal exists."

So on and on they went, day after day, and Cadmus saw that as each hour dragged by, his mother was becoming weaker and weaker. At last she began to stumble, and Cadmus caught her in his sturdy arms as she was falling to the ground. "Listen, my son," she gasped as he held her close to him. "I can go on no more. I must close my eyes in sleep, and I know that I shall not awaken. But you must go on, my son, till you have news of your sister. You must keep your vow and not try to return till you have found out what has happened to her. If you find her, tell her how I sought her until I could seek no more."

As she said this, the weary grief-stricken Telephassa closed her eyes, and Cadmus, with tears in his eyes, watched his mother until she ceased to breathe. All night long he held her in his arms, hoping against hope that by some miracle she might open her eyes and live again, but when the dawn came, he was left in no doubt that there was no life in the still form.

Sadly he placed his mother's body in the ground, and as he stood beside the grave, he vowed once again that he would not give up the search for his sister until she had been found.

So Cadmus continued his search alone, asking all those he met if they had seen any sign of the white bull, or of the girl on its back. As before, however, it seemed a hopeless quest, for no one had seen or even heard of the creature. Still he continued, becoming weaker and weaker, dragging his weary feet, but going ever onward, fiercely determined to keep his promise.

Now it happened that Apollo, the god of the sun, had seen what Zeus had done, and felt very sorry for the grieving Cadmus, who had not only lost his beloved sister, but also his mother. "I will help the youth," said Apollo, "for surely he has suffered enough. I will put an end to his vain search."

As Cadmus was patiently plodding along on his way, Apollo suddenly appeared before him. He was dressed in shining gold. In his hand was a bow of pure gold, and he carried a golden quiver full of golden arrows. Rays of light darted from him in all directions, and his face was as bright as the sun. Cadmus was startled at first at the sight of the gleaming figure, but remembering his vow, he plucked up courage to speak. He asked Apollo if he had seen any sign of the bull or of his sister.

"I have seen your sister," replied the god. "I saw her being carried away by the white bull. I know, too, of your vow, but I fear that you will never find her, for she is beyond the reach of any mortal. The bull was none other than the god Zeus himself, who has taken her to be his wife. Give up your search therefore, for though you may travel to the ends of the earth, you will never find her.

"You, however, because of your noble character, have been chosen to be a great king. Follow my instructions carefully, and the blessing of the gods will come upon you.

"You must keep on your way until you come to the town of Delphi, which lies at the foot of the great mountain of Parnassus. You will find in Delphi a great temple, which you must enter. There you will be given further instructions. Heed the voice which will speak to you there, but give up this search for your sister, for it is in vain."

As Apollo spoke, he smiled upon Cadmus, who felt a warm comforting glow inside him. His weariness seemed to have disappeared. His heart seemed much happier and his step much lighter as he went on his way towards the towering mountain of Parnassus, which he could see in the distance.

He strode on, until after some time he arrived at the beautiful temple of Delphi. He entered it, feeling rather nervous as to what would happen.

As he stood there looking about him, a faint whisper swept round the pillared walls, sounding just like the sighing breeze that gently moves the branches of the scented orange trees on a summer's day. Then faintly could be heard the sound of singing becoming louder and louder, until a chorus of heavenly voices filled the air and seemed to go deep down into his very soul. At last the voices gradually faded away and all was still once again.

Then a deep booming voice seemed to echo all around him, and his heart leapt at the sound. "O Cadmus," said the voice, "welcome to the temple of Delphi. You are destined to become a great and noble king, and ruler over a great city. Heed well my words. When you leave this temple, go on until you see a cow lying down in a field. This is a sign from the gods, for as you approach, the cow will rise and guide you to the place where you must build. There you must build many houses and buildings. Build them big and strong, for over that city you will reign, and become famous throughout the land." The voice ceased as suddenly as it had begun, and again all was still.

Cadmus lost no time in following the instructions which had been given to him. He left the temple and made his way towards the city of Phocis. As he approached, he saw a cow lying down in a field directly in his path. The animal watched him draw near, then stood up and wandered slowly off, turning its head from time to time, to see if Cadmus was following. On and on it went, quite a long way, until at last it came to rest on a large and grassy plain.

"This must be the place chosen by the gods," thought Cadmus; "here I will build the city." He set to work with a will, and people flocked from all around to help him. He built many fine houses and large, beautiful temples. He called his city Thebes, and became its first king.

It is said that he ruled so well that the gods allowed him to marry a beautiful goddess named Harmonia, and that many children were born to them. He was famous throughout the whole of Greece for his wise laws, and for his fondness for writing them down. Indeed many people say that he was the inventor of the Greek alphabet.

He ruled over Thebes for many years, and when he and Harmonia were very old, they fell into a deep sleep and were taken by the gods to the Islands of the Blessed.

The Legend of Psyche

Long, long ago, there lived a king of Greece who had several very beautiful daughters. One of these, however, was fairer than her sisters, and was beloved by all who knew her. Her name was Psyche, and so famed was she for her beauty that even the goddess Aphrodite was jealous of her. People would say that Psyche was even more beautiful than the goddess of beauty herself, and this made Aphrodite very angry indeed.

She called her son, Eros, and said, "This mortal woman is very impudent, and must be taught that she is not greater than the gods in any way. You must use your powers to make her fall in love with the ugliest, most wicked and most horrible person you can find." Now Eros was the youngest of the gods. He was winged, and very handsome, but he was fond of playing all sorts of tricks upon both gods and people, causing a great deal of trouble and sorrow. He was faithful to his mother, however, and Aphrodite was certain that he would do as she had asked.

Not long after this, the father of Psyche had a strange dream in which he saw the figure of a god standing before him. Then he heard a voice which said, "This is the command of the gods. Your daughter Psyche, whom you love so dearly, must be taken to the top of Mount Athrys, and there you must leave her to whatever fate is decided for her by the gods. She must not be dressed in any finery, but in the rough clothing of the serving women, and let there be a procession of people weeping and wailing for her. Do this and all will be well with you, but do not dare to defy the decree of the gods lest evil befall you."

The king and his daughters were in great distress, but the command had to be obeyed. Poor Psyche was dressed in old clothing and carried up to the top of the mountain, amid the weeping and wailing of the family and their devoted servants. There she was left alone in the darkness, wondering what dreadful thing was going to happen to her.

As she lay on a rock, weeping and sobbing as if her heart would break, she found herself being gently lifted up. She did not know that Zephyrus, the god of the west wind, was carrying her gently in his arms. As she was borne along, she felt as if a sweet-scented summer breeze were carrying the perfume of a thousand flowers towards her, and she felt strangely happy.

Zephyrus laid her gently down on a bed of flowers in a beautiful valley, and there she fell into a deep and peaceful slumber. When she awoke next morning, she found herself in a pleasant meadow through which flowed a sparkling stream.

As she looked around her, she saw nearby a most beautiful palace, built of gold and ivory. There were lovely domes and pillars adorned with precious stones, and indeed the whole of the palace gleamed and glistened in the sun, as if it were one massive jewel.

Psyche was enchanted by the beauty of the magnificent palace, and hesitantly she began to walk towards it. As she approached, she was amazed to hear a voice speaking to her in sweet, gentle tones. "Fear not, O gentle maiden," said the voice, "but enter the palace and use it as your home. Here you may dwell in happiness and sweet contentment, for all that you see is yours. Here you will be served as befits a princess. Enter then, O maiden, for you are safe from any harm."

The princess was amazed, but plucking up courage, she entered, and found herself in a huge hall. In the center of the hall was a fountain from which gushed sparkling water, cascading as it fell into a large marble bath. The floor was inlaid with gold, and around the walls were carvings of strange animals.

There was the sound of pleasant music, but though she roamed about from room to room, not one person or living creature did she see. She bathed herself, and feeling very much refreshed, she stepped out of the bath to find that some beautiful clothing had been placed in readiness for her to wear. She put on the clothing, and wandered into another room, where she saw that a table had been set for a meal. It was covered with all sorts of attractive dishes, and Psyche, who by now was feeling very hungry, sat down to the most sumptuous meal she had ever enjoyed.

As the day went on, she became used to the idea of being served by invisible hands. No sooner did she express a wish than it was carried out, and she began to feel that she was being cared for by some mysterious being who loved her very much. At night she lay down to sleep, and was just going to close her eyes in peaceful slumber when she felt the gentle touch of a hand upon her cheek.

She started up in alarm, but could see nothing in the darkness. "Who is there?" she called out.

"Be not afraid," said a voice, "for I am the husband chosen for you. I will love and protect you, and you can live in this palace forever. Do not seek to look upon my face, however, nor yet to know my name, for then great evil will befall you. Trust in me and you will always be happy."

Now Psyche was greatly comforted by the warm, gentle voice, and was happier than she had ever been in her life. As the days went by, she found herself longing for the night to come, when she would be with her husband, whom she imagined must be as handsome as he was kind. In her eagerness to be with him, she found the days beginning to drag, and she began to wish that she had her sisters with her. She could then show them this wonderful palace, and be able to talk with them during the long days when her husband was not with her.

When her husband came that night, he heard her sighing and he asked her what the matter was. "I love you dearly," she said, "and long each day for the night to come, so that you will be with me again. But the longing makes the days seem to drag, and I begin to feel lonely in the long summer hours. If only I could have my sisters with me, then I could talk to them, and the days would pass swiftly."

"I will ask the west wind to bring your sisters here," he replied, "for I can see that you are sad and lonely without them. Remember, however, that you must not allow them to persuade you to try to find out who I am. Believe me, O my beloved Psyche, from the moment when you try to see me, your troubles will begin." You may be sure that Psyche readily promised to do as he wished, for she was eager to see her sisters again.

Next morning, as Psyche's sisters were walking in the grounds of their father's palace, there came a strong gust of wind which lifted them off their feet. Then they felt themselves being gently carried through the air. After a short time, they were put down in front of the palace in which Psyche dwelt. You can imagine their surprise and delight when they saw their lost sister running towards them.

Great was their amazement when they saw the magnificent palace and all that it contained. Soon their happiness changed to jealousy, and they asked Psyche who her husband was.

"He must be a great prince indeed to possess all this wealth," they said, "for such luxury we have never seen before."

"I cannot tell you what you ask," said their sister, "for though I love my husband very dearly, I have never seen him. He comes at night, and I hear his gentle voice, but he has warned me never to try to discover who he is."

Now her sisters were by this time almost consumed with jealousy, so they said, "This creature who comes only at night and fears to be seen in the light of day must be some dreadful monster. You must find out who he is, for of a surety he will sooner or later do you harm. When he comes at night, light a lamp and see his face. You will find that what we say is true, and that he is indeed some hideous monster who can behave and speak gently when he pleases."

At first Psyche was not persuaded by her jealous sisters, but their words made her very sad, and the thought entered her mind that perhaps they were right. Day after day she worried about it, and at last could bear the uncertainty no longer. She made up her mind that she was going to find out who her husband really was.

One night, as her husband lay sleeping, she lit a lamp and looked down on the sleeping form. She saw no hideous monster as her sisters had foretold, but a most handsome god with golden hair and shining wings. At the foot of the couch lay his bow and arrows, and she knew at once that she was looking at Eros himself. She was so delighted that she peered forward to have a closer look at the handsome features, forgetting in her eagerness that she carried a lamp of burning oil.

As she bent over the sleeping form, a drop of hot oil fell onto his shoulder, and he awoke immediately. "O foolish Psyche," he said, "why did you break your promise to me? I came from Olympus to be your husband because I loved you so dearly, and now you have broken your trust. I must go now and will not return. Did I not warn you many times?"

As he said this, the son of Aphrodite took up his bow and arrows, spread his wings, and soared upwards until he had disappeared. At that moment, too, there came a clap of thunder, and the palace had vanished. Poor Psyche found herself once again on the lonely rock at the top of the mountain where she had been left by her father's servants. Her fine clothes had gone, and she was as miserable as could be.

"It was wicked of me," she wailed, "to listen to the false advice of my sisters, and to forget my promise to the most gentle husband in the world. How can I live without him?" Her heart was broken, and in despair she threw herself into a river which flowed down the mountainside. The waters, however, would not let her drown, but carried her gently to the opposite bank, where she lay on a bed of scented herbs.

"Seek not to destroy yourself," said a voice, and looking up she saw Pan, the god of the shepherds, seated on a rock nearby. "You may yet regain the love of Eros," he said, "but not by destroying yourself, or causing yourself harm. Go out into the world and do service for others. Search for Eros, and you may find him once again. Perhaps, because of your good deeds, he may come back to you again."

The son of Aphrodite took up his bow and
arrows, spread his wings, and soared upwards

The sorrowing maiden listened to the words of the shepherd god, and wandered about the country, helping people whenever she could, and searching always for the husband she had lost.

Now all this time Aphrodite had been very angry because her son Eros had disappointed her and had not carried out her wishes. He had been kind to Psyche instead of punishing her. "Now that she is alone," said the goddess, "I will punish her myself and give her such tasks to perform that she will regret ever having roused my anger." Of course the poor maiden had no idea that she had caused Aphrodite to be jealous of her beauty, and she went on her way quite innocent of the fact that she had caused a quarrel between the goddess and her son.

At last, faint and weary, Psyche made up her mind to pray to Aphrodite for help. "When she knows of my great love for Eros, I am sure she will be merciful and help me to find him," she thought. As Psyche prayed, she suddenly saw the goddess standing before her.

"I am not pleased that you desire my help to find Eros," she said, "but because my heart is merciful, and I know that my son loves you, I will set you some tasks to perform. If you do these well, I shall know that your love is true.

"Follow the path upon which you are walking, and you will come to a house. In this house you will find a great mixture of seeds of all kinds. These you must separate into different heaps, each according to their kind, and this you must do before the sun-god lights the dawn sky. When you have done this, I will appear before you again."

Aphrodite then departed, and Psyche found herself alone once again. She went along the path as she had been directed, and soon came to a large house, which she entered. There upon the floor lay an enormous heap of seeds all mixed together. There were wheat, barley, and poppy seeds and many others.

"It is impossible to separate all these," said the girl. "It would take many people several weeks to do this, so how can I do it in one night?" The poor maiden sat down and wept bitterly, for it was quite plain that Aphrodite did not intend her to carry out the task successfully.

Unknown to her, however, Eros was watching over her, and he called upon the ants to help her. "You busy creatures who toil without rest," he said, "help a maiden in distress." Then there came a great multitude of ants, so many that the floor was covered with them, and they toiled away all night, sorting and arranging the seeds into orderly piles, until it was all done. Before the first peep of dawn, they were gone, and as Psyche opened her eyes, sore from weeping, she gave a gasp of amazement, for there were the seeds arranged as Aphrodite had requested.

As the sun rose in the heavens, the goddess appeared again, and when she saw that the first task had been completed, she said, "This is not thine own work, O maiden, but that of my son. We shall see how you fare with the next task I set you. Beyond the house is a meadow, surrounded by a hedge of thorns. In this meadow are flocks of sheep whose fleeces are of gold. No shepherd watches over these sheep, and you must bring me some of the golden wool from their fleeces. This task also must be completed before dawn tomorrow."

Psyche arose immediately and made her way towards the meadow. The west wind, Zephyrus, was watching over the safety of the maiden, for he had been asked to do so by Eros. As she walked along, he caused the reeds to sway. They seemed to be talking in a musical way, and she stopped for a moment to listen to the voices. "Go not to the sheep in the bright rays of the sun," they said, "for then the sheep are fierce and will surely slay you. That indeed is the desire of Aphrodite. Wait until the sun-god dips his wings over the western horizon, and then they will not attack you. Gather some wool which the sheep have left among the thorns, and take that to Aphrodite."

Psyche listened to the voice of the wind in the reeds, and waited until sunset. Then she went into the meadow and safely gathered a handful of wool from the thicket around it. This she gave to Aphrodite when she appeared again next day. Now the goddess showed her displeasure by speaking unkind words to the girl. "Again I see that you have been helped in your task," she said, "but I will give you yet another task, which you will not find so easy to perform.

"At the foot of yonder hill flows a stream. It is one of the streams which feed the great river Acheron that tumbles down into Hades itself. Take this flask and bring some of the water of that stream."

Now this task did not seem difficult, and Psyche took the flask and made her way to the stream. To her dismay, however, she saw a number of great dragons near the water. She was afraid to go near lest they attack her. As she stood there, a great eagle swooped down and seized the flask from her trembling hand. It soared high above the dragons, and then swiftly descending upon the water, dipped the flask in it, and rose again.

With a great flapping of its giant wings, the eagle carried the flask to the girl and immediately flew off again. Of course, as you can guess, this too was done with the help of Eros, and when the maiden brought the flask to Aphrodite, the goddess was wild with anger.

"Still another task will I set you," she said. "This time you must go to Persephone, Queen of the Underworld. You must ask her to give you some of the magic ointment which makes beautiful those who use it. This ointment you must bring to me."

This was indeed a task which Psyche thought she could never perform. She knew full well that people did not return from Hades, once they had entered the Kingdom of the Underworld. "It is easy to see that Aphrodite wishes me to die," she wept, "and I shall never see my husband again. It would be far better to end my life now than to go on performing tasks each one more perilous than the last, for I must surely die in the end."

She made her way to the top of a very high tower and was just about to throw herself from it, when she heard a murmuring noise, as if the very stones of the tower were speaking. The noise became words, and suddenly she realized that they were being spoken to her. "Your tasks will soon be over," she was told. "Do not harm yourself, but go to Persephone as you have been commanded. Take with you two pieces of bread and honey and put two oboli in your mouth. With one of these coins you must pay Charon, the ferryman to Hades, to take you across the river, and with the other pay him when you return. The pieces of bread dipped in honey are to give to the dog, Cerberus, the three-headed creature which guards the gates of the Underworld. He will then allow you to enter. If you plead with Persephone, she will give you the box of ointment. Do not open the box, however, for if you do, you will pass into endless sleep."

The voice ceased as suddenly and as mysteriously as it had begun, and Psyche went to do as she had been told.

She succeeded in obtaining the box of ointment and brought it back with her from the depths of the Underworld. She became very curious, however, and thought that she would open the box, in spite of the warning she had received. Overcome by her curiosity, even as Aphrodite had expected, the maiden opened the box. To her surprise, she could not see anything in it, but as she looked she felt very drowsy, and soon fell into a deep sleep.

This was indeed the sleep of death, and Psyche would have passed back again into the Kingdom of the Underworld forever had not Eros decided to return to her at last. He spread his wings and flew down to her. Touching her eyes with his hand, he wiped away the sleep of death, and she awoke.

"Take the box to my mother," he said, "for the task must be completed, and I will go to Zeus, who dwells on Mount Olympus. I will plead with him and ask that we be allowed to live together among the gods."

Now Zeus in his mercy listened to the pleadings of Eros, and persuaded Aphrodite to forget her anger and hatred. Psyche was taken to heaven, and a great feast was arranged for the wedding of the two lovers who would never again be separated.

Tell me, O West Wind, what song do you sing?
When you sway the long reeds, what news do you bring?
Do you sing of a palace of marble and gold,
Where Psyche loved one whom she ne'er could behold?
When Pan plays his pipes by the swift mountain stream,
When he charms the mute sheep as they wander and dream,
Does he tell of the pain of a sorrowing maid,
Who lay nigh to death in a dark woodland glade?
When the great eagle soars from his lofty height,
Then swoops and dives and wheels in his flight,
What sees his keen eye in the valley below?
Is it Psyche who stands by the waters that flow,
Winding gloomily down to the land of the dead,
And guarded by dragons, their black wings outspread?
When the heights of Olympus are covered with cloud,
When the home of the gods they discreetly enshroud,
Has Zeus forgiven the sins of the past?
Are Psyche and Eros united at last?